Mr Big was a giant.

He was a very, very big giant.

He lived in a big house with big windows and
a big door.

One day Mr Big went to the park.

At the park Mr Big saw a red swing.
'I like swings,' he said. 'Can I go on
that swing?'
The children looked at Mr Big.
He was very, very, very big.
So they said,

Next, Mr Big saw a slide.

'I like slides,' he said. 'Can I go on that slide?'

The children looked at Mr Big.

He was very, very, very big.

So they said,

5

Next, Mr Big saw a roundabout.

'I like roundabouts,' he said. 'Can I go on that roundabout?'

The children looked at Mr Big.

He was very, very, very big.

So they said,

Mr Big was sad.

'What can I go on?' he said.

The children looked at Mr Big.

Then they looked at the bouncy castle.

It was very, very big.

'You can go on the bouncy castle,' they said.

And Mr Big said,

Yippee!